A BARNABY AND HOOKER GRAPHIC NOVEL

DARK HORSE BOOKS

WRITTEN BY **JANET** AND **ALEX EVANOVICH**
DRAWN BY **JOËLLE JONES**

BACKGROUND PENCILS **BEN DEWEY** | INKS **ANDY OWENS** | COLORS **DAN JACKSON** | LETTERS **NATE PIEKOS OF BLAMBOT**®

**For Barnaby,
the greatest St. Bernard
a girl could have.**

President & Publisher
MIKE RICHARDSON

Editor
SIERRA HAHN

Assistant Editor
FREDDYE LINS

Collection Designer
DAVE NESTELLE

Special thanks to Anita Nelson and Dark Horse Comics for giving us the opportunity to make a lifelong dream come true.

Thanks also to Matt Dryer and Lia Ribacchi.

executive vice president Neil Hankerson • chief financial officer Tom Weddle • vice president of publishing Randy Stradley • vice president of business development Michael Martens • vice president of business affairs Anita Nelson • vice president of marketing Micha Hershman • vice president of product development David Scroggy • vice president of information technology Dale LaFountain • director of purchasing Darlene Vogel • general counsel Ken Lizzi • editorial director Davey Estrada • senior managing editor Scott Allie • senior books editor Chris Warner • executive editor Diana Schutz • director of design and production Cary Grazzini • art director Lia Ribacchi • director of scheduling Cara Niece

Published by Dark Horse Books
A division of Dark Horse Comics, Inc.
10956 SE Main Street
Milwaukie, OR 97222

www.DarkHorse.com
www.Evanovich.com
www.JoelleJones.com

To find a comics shop in your area, call the Comic Shop Locator Service toll-free at (888) 266-4226.

First edition: July 2011
ISBN 978-1-59582-830-9

10 9 8 7 6 5 4 3 2 1
Printed at 1010 Printing International, Ltd., Guangdong Province, China

HOW TO READ A GRAPHIC NOVEL

Just because *Troublemaker* is Janet's first foray into graphic novels, that doesn't mean her prose fans can't get the same amount of enjoyment when they pick up a copy of this best-selling book!

A good graphic novel tells a story in two ways: images and text. Both of these elements contribute equally to the amount of storytelling on each page. That is to say, readers of graphic novels should note that the images in each panel tell as much story as the text does.

Although graphic novels look different than typical prose novels, the text and panels flow in roughly the same pattern: top to bottom, and left to right.

Follow the dialogue from one speech bubble to the next. Typically, you can follow the dialogue easily by letting your eye float to whatever bubble is closest to the one you last read within any given panel.

Try spending as much time looking at the images within each panel as you do reading the text and dialogue. See what you like most about enjoying sequential art, and focus on what draws you into the story the most.

Don't be surprised if a character isn't describing an action or an emotion. That's what the images are for! Let the character's body language and panel environments tell you what else is going on.

TROUBLEMAKER

Chapter One

MY NAME IS ALEX BARNABY. I ONCE STOLE AN EIGHTEEN-WHEELER AND DROVE IT TO MIAMI.

MY FRIEND, FELICIA, LET ME HIDE AND DISMANTLE THE TRUCK IN HER EMPTY WAREHOUSE.

AND OUR FRIEND, ROSA REMOVED THE DEAD BODY THAT WAS IN THE EIGHTEEN-WHEELER'S STORAGE COMPARTMENT.

FOR THE RECORD, I DIDN'T *KILL* THE GUY. I JUST FOUND HIM.

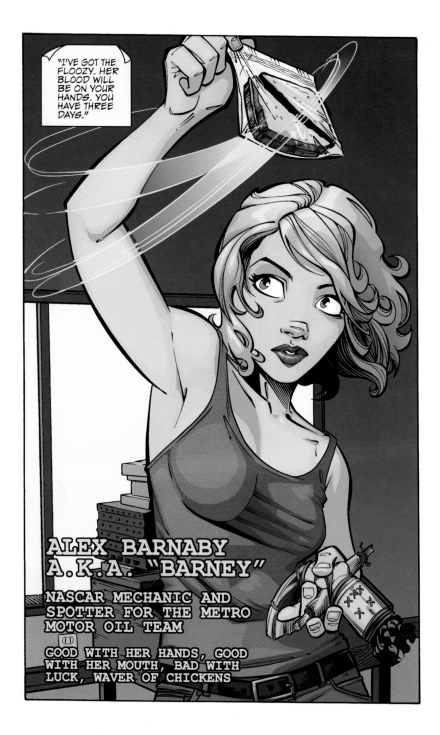

FOR THE RECORD I'D ALSO LIKE TO SAY...

...I WAS NEVER INVOLVED IN KIDNAPPINGS AND DOG-NAPPINGS...

...ATTACKED BY GIANT SPIDERS...

...OR HAD BAD JUJU THRUST UPON ME...

...UNTIL SAM HOOKER ENTERED MY LIFE.

32

THE KIND OF BAD FEELING THAT COMES FROM TOUCHING SOMEONE ELSE'S HALF-EATEN HOT DOGS AND MOLDY CHEESE.

MAYBE HE'S POTASSIUM DEFICIENT.

THE KIND OF BAD FEELING THAT SAYS, "THEY DON'T MAKE A TIDE STICK BIG ENOUGH."

40

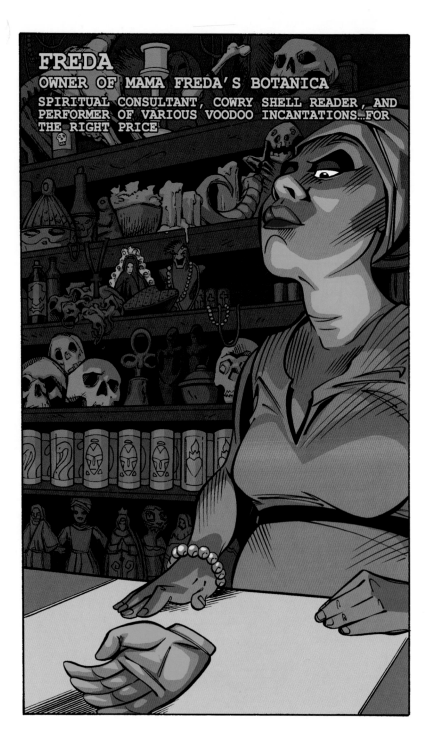

IT'S A HAND.

WE'RE HOPING YOU CAN TELL US WHOSE.

IT BELONGS TO A SACRED STATUE OF BARON SAMEDI...

...THE LOA OF DEATH.

BAD JUJU, HUH?

BAD PEOPLE.

THE PAPER IS FROM AN UNDERGROUND BOTANICA IN LITTLE HAITI.

THEY ONLY DEAL WITH PETRO VOODOO WORSHIPERS. AND I USE "VOODOO" ONLY IN THE MOST BASIC SENSE.

MORE LIKE A BLACK-MAGIC CULT.

52

"WITH THE COMING OF THE FULL MOON...."

...THEY WILL BE PERFORMING *MANGÉ LOA*.

"AT *MIDNIGHT*, GO TO THE SWAMP."

57

59

FIRST THERE WAS A VOODOO-DOLL BOMB.

THEN HOOKER'S MOM GAVE ME THE THIRD DEGREE.

FOLLOWED BY HOOKER AND ME COMMITTING THE FEDERAL OFFENSE OF STEALING MAIL.

AND THE DEAL IS SEALED WITH BEING CHASED BY AN ANGRY CULT THROUGH THE EVERGLADES IN A FAN BOAT.

THAT NOISE?

Uh...I'M NOT FEELING SO GOOD.

HOLD ON!

VROOM

CHAOS. PANIC. DISORDER. I GUESS MY WORK HERE IS DONE.

YOUR MOM WANTS YOU TO CALL HER BACK.

OVER THE YEARS I'VE LEARNED THAT THERE ARE A COUPLE REASONS, OTHER THAN "BEING NOSY IS FUN," TO SNOOP IN A MISSING PERSON'S HOUSE.

I'LL CHECK UPSTAIRS.

ONE IS TO SEE IF THE PERSON LEFT WILLINGLY.

TOOTHBRUSH AND SHAVING STUFF STILL HERE. DISAPPEARING WASN'T PLANNED.

AND THE SECOND IS TO SEE IF ANYONE ELSE IS LOOKING FOR YOUR MISSING PERSON.

EITHER PERCY IS A TOTAL PIG, OR WE AREN'T THE FIRST TO BREAK INTO HIS HOUSE.

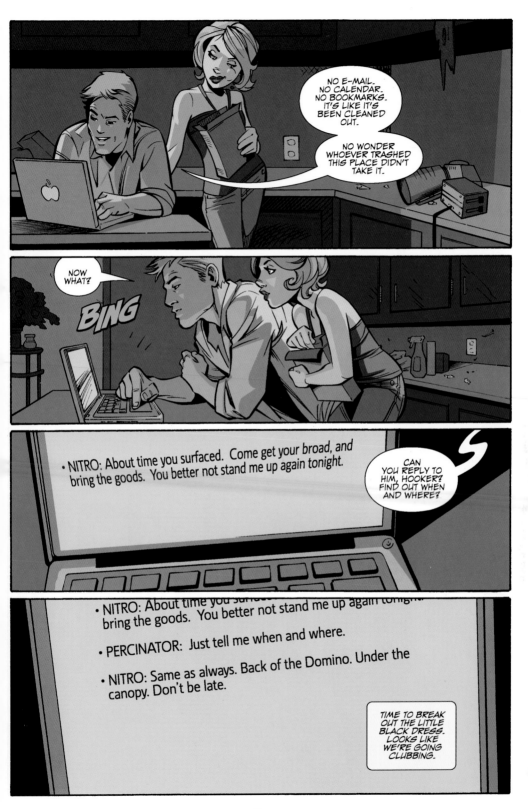

84

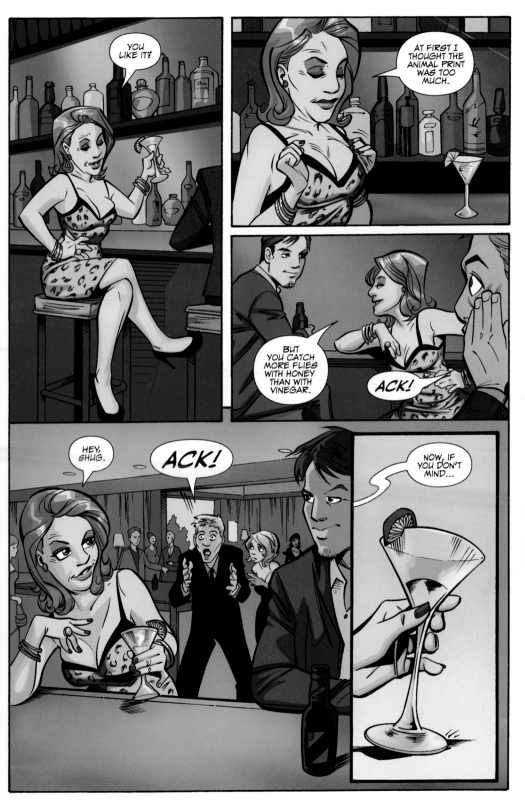

89

91

I PAID PERCY TO HOLD ONTO A RATHER *RARE* ITEM I RECENTLY ACQUIRED.

NOW I WANT IT BACK.

IT'S A MOLDY, OLD STATUE OF SOME VOODOO DUDE.

WHAT? WAS THAT A SECRET?

I'LL GIVE YOU TWENTY-FOUR HOURS TO GET MY MESSAGE TO PERCY.

CHEESE IT!

GO, GREEN, GREEN, *GREEN!*

WHAT THE HECK WERE YOU TWO THINKING? YOU COME TO RESCUE ME WITH A TWO-SEATER?

ARE THESE REAL LEATHER?

IT'S THE FASTEST CAR I HAVE, AND I KNEW THE VALET WOULD LEAVE IT OUT FRONT.

WATCH WHERE YOU'RE PUTTING YOUR KNEE.

PERCY WAS TRYING REAL HARD TO GET A WOMAN TO TALK TO HIM, BUT HE HAS THAT RAT-FACE PROBLEM. IT WAS KIND OF PATHETIC, SO I THOUGHT I WOULD SIT WITH HIM FOR A BIT.

YOU KNOW... *PITY*, PLUS I COULD REALLY USE A RAISE.

KEEP YOUR SHIRT ON. I'M SETTING THE MOOD.

ROSA, WHERE IS THIS STORY GOING? GET TO THE STATUE.

SO I'M SITTING, TALKING TO PERCY IN THE FLAMINGO, AND MR. VOODOO COMES IN. PERCY ALWAYS CALLED HIM NITRO, BUT I THINK THE GUY'S *REAL* NAME IS *ARMANDO DUPOINT*.

ANYWAY, WHEN NITRO SAT DOWN AT OUR TABLE, PERCY GAVE ME A TWENTY AND ASKED ME TO GO GET US SOME DRINKS. LIKE I WAS HIS WOMAN.

I FIGURED I'D PLAY ALONG, 'CAUSE LIKE I SAID, I COULD REALLY USE A RAISE.

NOBODY PANIC. WE'RE HEADING FOR THE INTERSTATE.

IT'S A GOOD THING I CAN'T SEE WHERE WE'RE GOING, HUH?

YES!

103

TO THE FLORIDA KEYS IT IS.

TROUBLEMAKER

Chapter Five

HOOKER, ROSA, FELICIA, AND I TOOK HOOKER'S BOAT DOWN TO KEY WEST BECAUSE ROSA INSISTED WE HELP HER BOSS, WALTER PERCY.

WALTER WAS BABY-SITTING A STATUE OF SOME VOODOO GUY NAMED BARON SAMEDI WHEN HE FOUND OUT IT WAS STOLEN FROM A MUSEUM. WHEN HE REFUSED TO GIVE IT BACK TO THE ORIGINAL THIEF, NITRO, THINGS TURNED UGLY.

JUDGING FROM OUR PAST EXPERIENCE WITH NITRO, THERE ISN'T MUCH HE WOULDN'T DO TO GET THAT STATUE BACK.

SO WE'RE HERE TO RESCUE WALTER, HELP RETURN THE BARON TO THE MUSEUM, AND HOPEFULLY ENJOY THE REST OF OUR VACATION.

KEYWEST BIGHT
SLIP D-12

HOOKER... WHERE'S YOUR BOAT?

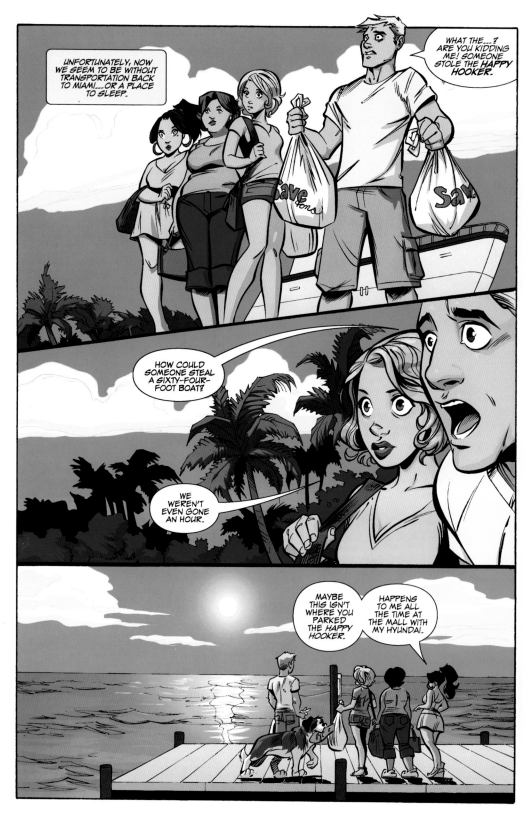

110

WE KNOW, AND WE WANT TO HELP YOU RETURN THE BARON TO THE MUSEUM, BUT WE HAVE ANOTHER PROBLEM.

UNFORTUNATELY, A FEW HOURS AGO, NITRO STOLE MY EXTREMELY EXPENSIVE SIXTY-FOUR-FOOT HATTERAS THAT I DEARLY LOVE, AND HE'S HOLDING IT FOR RANSOM.

WE NEED YOU TO HELP US GET MY BOAT BACK FIRST, WALTER.

I'M SORRY TO HEAR ABOUT YOUR BOAT, AND I'D LIKE TO HELP YOU, BUT I'M NOT SURE WHAT I CAN DO...

OOF!

I'M GOING TO GIVE YOU ONE MORE CHANCE TO TELL US THE TRUTH...

...WHAT'S THE DEAL WITH THE HAND?

YEAH, WALTER. WHY TAKE THE BARON'S HAND OFF IF YOU WANT TO RETURN HIM TO THE MUSEUM?

SNGRX

I WASN'T GOING TO KEEP IT. I WAS GOING TO GIVE IT BACK WHEN I WAS DONE WITH IT.

NOT MY HAIR! OKAY! I'LL TALK! I'LL TALK!

THE HAND IS THE KEY TO BURIED TREASURE.

WHEN I FOUND OUT THE BARON WAS STOLEN, I STARTED TO DO SOME ONLINE RESEARCH.

I READ A PAPER BY A STUDENT AT LOYOLA UNIVERSITY ABOUT AN ANCIENT WOODEN STATUE OF BARON SAMEDI THAT CAME FROM HAITI.

"SUPPOSEDLY A YOUNG HOUNGAN-- THAT'S A VOODOO PRIEST-- FROM HAITI ONCE TRAVELED TO THE TURKS AND CAICOS IN SEARCH OF THE PASSAGE-WAY BETWEEN THE LAND OF THE LIVING AND THE LAND OF THE DEAD."

"WHEN HE RETURNED HE HAD A SEED FROM A SACRED OAK TREE AND A KEY, MADE OF IRON."

LEGEND HAS IT THAT THE KEY BELONGED TO SPANISH EXPLORER PONCE DE LEÓN, AND IT UNLOCKS HIS TREASURE.

PONCE DE LEÓN HAD A TREASURE? YOU AREN'T TALKING ABOUT THE FOUNTAIN OF YOUTH, ARE YOU?

MAYBE. BUT I'D SETTLE FOR A CHEST OF GOLD AND JEWELS.

"SUPPOSEDLY THE YOUNG HOUNGAN PLANTED THE OAK SEED IN HALLOWED GROUNDS AND SPENT THE REMAINDER OF HIS YEARS GROWING A TREE AROUND THE KEY IN ORDER TO PROTECT IT.

"OVER ONE HUNDRED YEARS LATER THERE WAS A TERRIBLE STORM THAT BLEW THE SACRED OAK OVER. THE PRIEST'S SUCCESSOR, AND NEW GUARDIAN OF THE TREE CARVED THE FALLEN OAK INTO A LIFE-SIZE STATUE OF BARON SAMEDI IN ORDER TO PROTECT THE KEY INSIDE."

153

CRAK

174

EVERYONE KNOWS WHAT TO DO, RIGHT?

KEEP AN EYE ON YOU THROUGH THE BINOCULARS--

IF EVERYTHING GOES RIGHT, AS SOON AS YOU LEAVE NITRO'S CAMP, THE GIRLS PUT THE CHAIRS IN THE BOAT AND I SEND OUT AN EMERGENCY SIGNAL THROUGH THE TWO-WAY RADIO.

I LEAVE THE RADIO HERE WHILE WE HIGH-TAIL IT OUT OF THE SWAMP, AND HOPE THAT THE POLICE SHOW UP IN TIME TO GET NITRO AND THE BARON.

SORRY ABOUT NOT BEING ABLE TO GO AFTER THE TREASURE, WALTER.

THAT'S OKAY. I WOULDN'T KNOW WHERE TO START LOOKING ANYWAY. I JUST WANT TO DO THE RIGHT THING.

ARMANDO DUPOINT

OPERATES UNDER THE ALIAS OF NITRO

A BOKOR, A THIEF, AND A KIDNAPPER. HE OWNS
A FAST CAR AND AN ANGRY CHICKEN... ALTHOUGH
THOSE MIGHT BE STOLEN, TOO

197

199

IT SAYS HERE THAT AUTHORITIES WERE NOTIFIED OF A MASSIVE EXPLOSION IN THE EVERGLADES, WHERE THEY TOOK INTO CUSTODY AN ARMANDO DUPOINT ON CHARGES OF CARRYING AN ILLEGAL, NON-REGISTERED ROCKET LAUNCHER...

...OTHER CHARGES MAY BE PENDING.

IT'S A BAZOOKA, AND I DIDN'T WANT TO GET CAUGHT WITH THAT THING. I THREW IT INTO NITRO'S BOAT WHILE HE WAS FIGHTING WITH BARNEY. WHAT A LOSER. GUESS WE WON'T HAVE TO WORRY ABOUT HIM FOR A WHILE.

YEAH, BUT AT LEAST HE WASN'T A LIAR. THE *HAPPY/NASTY HOOKER* WAS SITTING IN ITS SLIP WHEN WE GOT HERE. JUST LIKE HE SAID IT WOULD BE.

CREATOR BIOGRAPHIES

Janet and her granddog, Barnaby.

JANET EVANOVICH is the number-one *New York Times* best-selling author of the Stephanie Plum series, as well as the Alex Barnaby and Sam Hooker series *Metro Girl* and *Motor Mouth*. Janet lives in Florida with her husband and her Havanese, Ollie. This is her first foray into writing comics.

ALEX EVANOVICH is the daughter of Janet Evanovich. She's been working with Janet for over fourteen years doing Internet work, newsletters, and editing, and is one of the coauthors of *How I Write*. She lives in Florida with her husband and her St. Bernard, Barnaby.

JOËLLE JONES debuted in comics in 2006, contributing a short story to the Dark Horse anthology *Sexy Chix*. She followed this a year later with the full graphic novel *12 Reasons Why I Love Her*, her first collaboration with author Jamie S. Rich. She then went on to illustrate the crime graphic novel *You Have Killed Me* and, most recently, the teen-witch comedy *Spell Checkers*. Joëlle has also drawn the youngadult book *Token* with Alisa Kwitney, worked with Zack Whedon on a comic-book spinoff of the popular *Dr. Horrible's Sing-Along Blog* web series, and drawn two issues of the Eisner-nominated series *Madame Xanadu*, written by Matt Wagner. She is currently working on a long-form comic for DC/Vertigo called *The Starving Artist*. You can visit her online at www.JoelleJones.com.

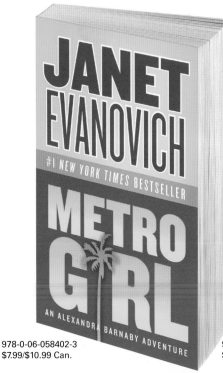
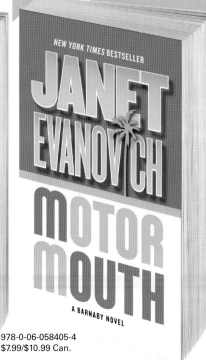

FROM DARK HORSE DELUXE . . .

TROUBLEMAKER PLAYING CARDS
$4.99
ISBN 978-1-61659-074-1

BEANS T-SHIRT
$24.99
ISBN 978-1-61659-089-5

LOGO AND PALM TREES T-SHIRT
$24.99
ISBN 978-1-61659-066-6

BARNABY AND HOOKER T-SHIRT
$24.99
ISBN 978-1-61659-069-7

RECOMMENDED
DARK HORSE READING...

BUFFY THE VAMPIRE SLAYER SEASON EIGHT VOLUME 1: THE LONG WAY HOME
JOSS WHEDON, GEORGES JEANTY

Since the destruction of the Hellmouth, the Slayers—newly legion—have gotten organized and are kicking some serious undead butt. But not everything's fun and firearms, as an old enemy reappears and Dawn experiences some serious growing pains. Meanwhile, one of the "Buffy" decoy slayers is going through major pain of her own.

Buffy creator Joss Whedon brings Buffy back to Dark Horse in this direct follow-up to season seven of the smash-hit TV series.
$15.99
ISBN 978-1-59307-822-5

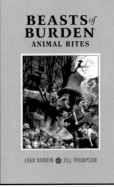

BEASTS OF BURDEN VOLUME 1: ANIMAL RITES
EVAN DORKIN, JILL THOMPSON

Welcome to Burden Hill—a picturesque little town adorned with white picket fences and green, green grass, home to a unique team of paranormal investigators. Beneath this shiny exterior, Burden Hill harbors dark and sinister secrets, and it's up to a heroic gang of dogs—and one cat—to protect the town from the evil forces at work. Can our heroes overcome these supernatural menaces? Can evil be bested by a paranormal team that doesn't have hands? And even more importantly, will Pugs ever shut the hell up?
$19.99
ISBN 978-1-59582-513-1

GIANT SIZE LITTLE LULU VOLUME 1
JOHN STANLEY, IRVING TRIPP

John Stanley and Irving Tripp's long run on *Little Lulu* is a milestone in American comics, as hilarious to grownups as it is to their children. With Stanley's popularity at an all-time high, Dark Horse is proud to take you back to the beginning of this legendary run. Collecting some of the earliest out-of-print volumes of Dark Horse's acclaimed reprint series, this massive 664-page omnibus contains the first fourteen issues where Little Lulu appeared.
$24.99
ISBN 978-1-59582-502-5

OH MY GODDESS! VOLUME 1
KOSUKE FUJISHIMA

Alone in his dorm, Nekomi Tech's Keiichi Morisato dials a wrong number that will change his life forever—reaching the Goddess Technical Help Line. Granted one wish by the charming young goddess Belldandy, Keiichi wishes she would stay with him always! Complications are bound to ensue from this; the immediate first being the new couple getting tossed out of the dorm—it's males only! How is his new "exchange student" companion going to be received on the NIT campus? A little too well for normal life to ever return . . .
$10.99
ISBN 978-1-59307-387-9